KEEP CALM AND COLOUR FOR MUMS

HUCK & PUCKER

For fast-acting relief,
try slowing down.

Lily Tomlin

If you can express your soul,
the rest ceases to matter.

Hugh MacLeod

Mother is the heartbeat in the home; and
without her, there seems to be no heart throb.

Leroy Brownlow

Art was made to overcome chaos.

Don Jones

Daydreaming with pencil
and paper is a respectable
form of meditation.

John Howe

Colour is my day-long obsession,
joy and torment.

Claude Monet

Mother's love is peace.
It need not be acquired,
it need not be deserved.

Erich Fromm

The reluctance to put away childish
things may be a requirement of genius.

Rebecca Pepper Sinkler

Man needs colour to live; it's just as necessary
an element as fire and water.

Fernand Léger

Who looks outside, dreams;
who looks inside, awakes.

Carl Jung

Colour is a power which directly
influences the soul.

Wassily Kandinsky

A mother is she who
can take the place of all
others but whose place
no one else can take.

Gaspard Mermillod

Some colours reconcile themselves to one another, others just clash.

Edvard Munch

Do not move, do not go. Sink within
this moment. Hold it for ever.

Virginia Woolf

There is no way to be a perfect mother,
and a million ways to be a good one.

Jill Churchill

Art is therapy for my soul.

Reno

Colours are the smiles of nature.

Leigh Hunt

Artists are just children who refuse to
put down their crayons.

Al Hirschfeld

Art enables us to find ourselves and
lose ourselves at the same time.

Thomas Merton

Put your heart, mind, and soul
into even your smallest acts.
This is the secret of success.

Sivananda Saraswati

For most exhausted mums,
their idea of 'working out' is
a good, energetic lie-down.

Kathy Lette

The purest and most thoughtful minds are
those which love colour the most.

John Ruskin

Why do two colours, put one
next to the other, sing?
Can one really explain this? No.

Pablo Picasso

Art is the journey of a free soul.

Alev Oguz

I cannot pretend to be impartial about the
colours. I rejoice with the brilliant ones, and
am genuinely sorry for the poor browns.

Winston Churchill

God could not be everywhere,
so he created mothers.

Jewish proverb

We need crayons and paper tucked
into important places in our lives.

Dr SunWolf

Drawing is one of the best ways to
meditate, while staying connected
to the world around us.

Elsha Leventis

It is a happy talent to know how to play.

Ralph Waldo Emerson

Happiness arises in a state of peace, not of tumult.

Ann Radcliffe

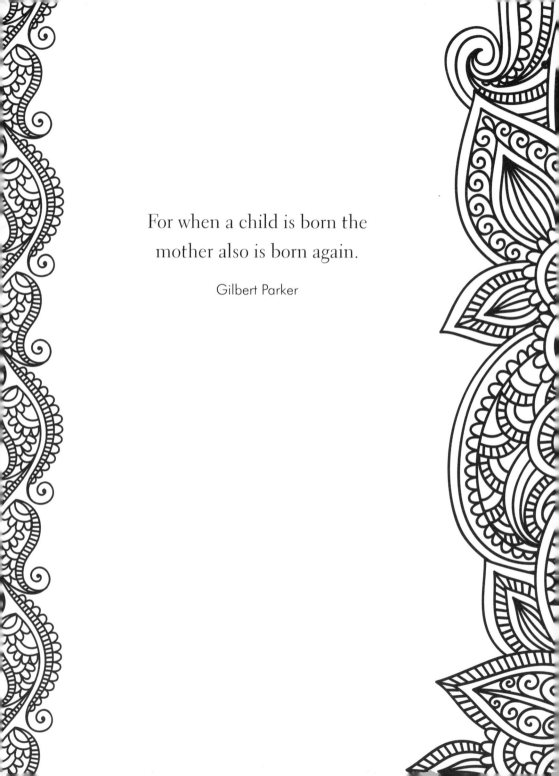

For when a child is born the
mother also is born again.

Gilbert Parker

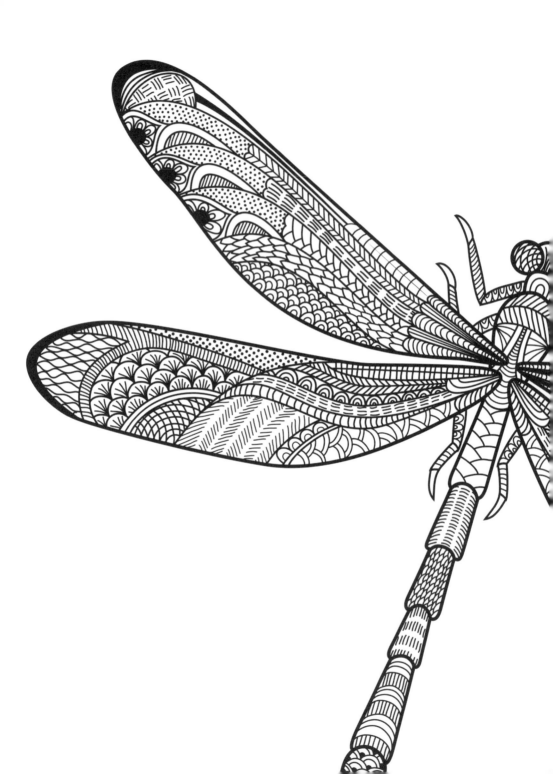

At the end of your brush is
the tip of your soul.

Andrew Hamilton

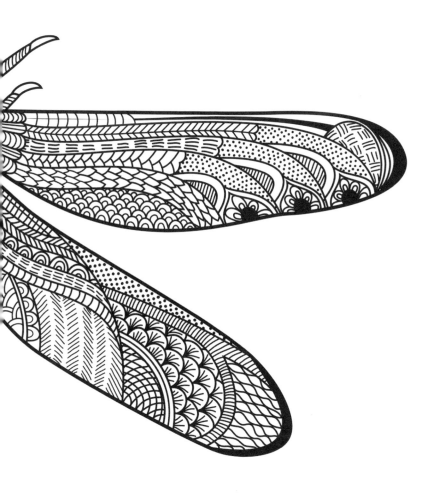

Red is passion-lit, orange is
flowerageous, yellow is suntastic, pink
is lipsensual, green is lifebursting, blue
is skyful, purple is berrydancing.

Terri Guillemets

Drawing is a frame of mind,
a loving embrace, if you will.

Susan Avishai

Creativity is a habit, and the best creativity
is the result of good work habits.

Twyla Tharp

To a child's ear, 'mother'
is magic in any language.

Arlene Benedict

Every production of an artist should be the
expression of an adventure of his soul.

W. Somerset Maugham

The pursuit, even of the best things,
ought to be calm and tranquil.

Cicero

On the sixth day, God created the artist, realising no doubt that He had far from exhausted the uses of colour.

Robert Brault

Be brave enough to live life
creatively. The creative place where
no one else has ever been.

Alan Alda

A mother's happiness is like a beacon,
lighting up the future but
reflected also on the past in the
guise of fond memories.

Honoré de Balzac

Colour is everything, colour
is vibration like music;
everything is vibration.

Marc Chagall

Put your ear down close to
your soul and listen hard.

Anne Sexton

Isn't it amazing what a
pencil can have inside?

Quino

Govern a family as you would
cook a small fish – very gently.

Chinese proverb

So, like a forgotten fire, a childhood
can always flare up again within us.

Gaston Bachelard

Be the calm centre in the
raging flow of life.

Leo Babauta

If you're interested in finding out
more about our products, find us on
Facebook at **HuckAndPucker** and
follow us on Twitter at @**HuckandPucker**.

www.huckandpucker.com

Huck & Pucker
Huck Towers
46 West Street
Chichester
West Sussex
PO19 1RP
UK

www.huckandpucker.com

Printed and bound in the Czech Republic

ISBN: 978-1-909865-13-6

Substantial discounts on bulk quantities of Huck & Pucker books are available to corporations, professional associations and other organisations. For details contact Nicky Douglas by telephone: +44 (0) 1243 756902, fax: +44 (0) 1243 786300 or email: huck@huckandpucker.com.